THE SPX 2005 ANTHOLOGY
PUBLISHED BY THE COMIC BOOK LEGAL DEFENSE FUND

EDITED BY BRIAN RALPH
ASSISTANT EDITORS: CHARLES BROWNSTEIN AND ELIZABETH GORDON
INSIDE FRONT & BACK COVER BY BRIAN CHIPPENDALE
FRONT COVER & BACK COVER ART BY BRIAN RALPH

PRODUCED BY THE EXPO TO BENEFIT THE COMIC BOOK LEGAL DEFENSE FUND.

EXPO 2005. ALL RIGHTS RESERVED. ALL COMICS STORIES © 2005 BY THEIR
RESPECTIVE CREATORS.
DESIGN/PRODUCTION: CHRIS PITZER, PITZER@ADHOUSEBOOKS.COM
THANKS TO TOP SHELF AND JOSE VILLARRUBIA

NO PART OF THIS BOOK (EXCEPT SMALL PORTION FOR REVIEW PURPOSES) MAY
BE USED WITHOUT EXPRESSED WRITTEN CONSENT FROM THE CBLDF.

ISBN 1-891830-79-1 PRINTED IN CANADA.

EXPO 2005 IS A BOOK COMPANION TO THE EXPO, A FESTIVAL OF CARTOONISTS AND
COMICS PUBLISHERS HELD ANNUALLY IN BETHESDA, MARYLAND.

ALL PROCEEDS FROM THE BOOK YOU NOW HOLD IN YOUR HANDS BENEFIT THE COMIC
BOOK LEGAL DEFENSE FUND AND HELP PROTECT FREE EXPRESSION IN COMICS.

TURN TO THE FINAL PAGES OF THIS BOOK FOR MORE INFORMATION
ON THE EXPO AND THE COMIC BOOK LEGAL DEFENSE FUND.

SPX 2005

TABLE OF CONTENTS

Brain BEAR

IN BATTLE BEAR

KEVIN SHERRY

THE END

WELL, THESE PARACHUTES ARE MADE OF FIBER-GLASS AND THE WHOLE PROCESS IS CONTROLLED BY COMPUTERS.

I DON'T SEE ANY DIFFERENCE... UNLESS THEY SOFTEN THE GROUND FOR YOU...

"OR YOUR BONES GET HARDER.

5

- 13 -

EN MEMORIA DEL MAESTRO EUGENIO ZOPPI

········· WWW.LAPRODUCTORA.COM.AR ·········· F. REGGIANI - A. MOSQUITO - 2005

BUT MY DAD WAS RIGHT. TURNING MY BACK ON THESE PIECES OF ACACIA WAS LIKE TURNING MY BACK ON MY FAMILY, MY HISTORY, MYSELF!

—HRUMPH!

THESE CARVINGS WERE HEIRLOOMS PASSED ON FROM MY ANCESTORS TO FUTURE GENERATIONS.

THE RICE FARMER THAT ALWAYS SAT ON OUR COFFEE TABLE PERSONIFIED THE COURAGE, STRENGTH, AND SACRIFICES MADE BY THOSE WHO CAME BEFORE ME.

SO I DECIDED TO EMBRACE THESE WOOD CARVINGS AND SHOW MY PRIDE FOR THEM BY FINALLY INVITING MY FRIENDS OVER MY HOUSE.

WHAT KIND OF DANCE ARE THEY DOING?

IT IS THE "DANCE OF JUBILATION."

HOW THE HECK SHOULD I KNOW?

BUT ONE DAY, I FOUND OUT SOMETHING STARTLING...

I LOOOVE YOUR LITTLE WOOD STATUES!

OH! YOU CAN BUY ONE FOR YOURSELF. WE GOT OURS FROM A THRIFT STORE!

WHAT?!?
YOU MEAN WE ACTUALLY PAID MONEY FOR THESE THINGS?!?

A NEXT-DOOR NEIGHBOR

THESE WERE NOT THE PRICELESS HEIRLOOMS I THOUGHT THEY WERE. IN FACT, OTHER FILIPINO FAMILIES HAD THE SAME CARVINGS THAT WE HAD TOO!

C'MON! MY MOM'S MAKING US PEANUT BUTTER & JELLY SANDWICHES!

UH...

HEY RINA!

AND A FEW HAD SOME RACY ONES LIKE THE ONE AT MY GREAT-UNCLE'S HOUSE.

WHY HELLO THERE...

DON'T EVEN THINK ABOUT IT!

EVENTUALLY I STOPPED TAKING OUR WOOD CARVINGS SO SERIOUSLY, AND STARTED TO LOOK AT THEM AS EVERYDAY HOUSEHOLD ITEMS.

TIME TO DIE, MY FRIEND.

HA! NOT UNTIL I DIG YOUR GRAVE FIRST!

THEIR MYSTIQUE DISAPPEARED, BUT THAT DIDN'T MEAN THAT WE STOPPED TAKING PRIDE IN THEM.

HEY! WHO PUT THAT UPSIDE-DOWN?

EW! LOOK! HE'S MOONING YOU, MOM ≡HEE-HEE≡

NOT ME, MOM!

THE END.

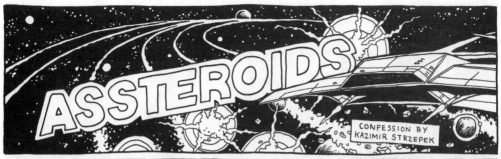

ASSTEROIDS

CONFESSION BY KAZIMIR STRZEPEK

HIGHSCORE!

HMM... MY OBSESSION WITH VIDEO GAMES BEGAN AT AGE 4, WHEN MY COUSIN ROBBIE HANDED DOWN HIS ATARI 2600 TO ME & MY SISTER.

THIS PANDORA'S BOX INCLUDED CLASSIC GAMES SUCH AS ADVENTURE, PONG, PITFALL, COMBAT & FROGGER.

AMELIA & I WOULD PLAY FOR HOURS. AND WHEN MOM & DAD SHOOED US OUTSIDE...

WAH WEE WAA WEWAAAAA

WE'D JUST IMITATE THEM AT THE PARK DOWN THE STREET.

Pitfall Harry

Alligator

GRAH!

PACA-PACA-PACMAN

shrivel

my brain...

Oh god, my brain.

VIDEO GAMES WERE ALWAYS ON MY MIND. I WOULD COPY THE ART FROM THE MANUALS, INCORPORATE CHARACTERS INTO MY CREATIVE WRITING HOMEWORK, MAKE MODELS OUT OF LEGOS & THE WORST WAS WHEN GOING TO THE BATHROOM...

It was all downhill from there.

MY IS D

KILL ME

2005 KAZIMIR

WHAT BEGAN AS AN ORDINARY DINNER OUT WITH THE FAMILY, ENDED UP BEING THE BIRTHPLACE OF ONE OF MY ODDEST HABITS THROUGHOUT MY ADOLESCENCE.

EXCUSE ME.

I HAFTA GO TO THE BATHROOM.

AS I ENTERED THE STALL, I FOUND THE PATRON BEFORE ME NEGLECTED TO FLUSH HIS EXCREMENT.

GAH!

INSTEAD OF DOING THE DECENT THING BY FLUSHING RIGHT AWAY... MY VIDEO GAME INFESTED BRAIN JUST SAT IN CEREBROSPINAL IDLE.

HOURS & HOURS OF ATARI VR TRAINING HAD PREPARED ME FOR THIS MOMENT.

I UNZIPPED, PULLED OUT MY PEE-PEE, TOOK AIM...

AND IT WAS THEN & THERE...

ASSTEROIDS WAS BORN!

⌐ special "Turd's-eye-view"

WITH MY STREAM OF URINE, I ATTEMPTED TO BREAK-UP THE TURDS AS QUICKLY AS POSSIBLE

IT WASN'T AN EASY TASK

300

FORTUNATELY I HAD A BLADDER FULL OF SODAPOP

OF COURSE THERE WAS POOP IN THE TOILET... AS WELL AS A FEW OTHER PLACES...

JEEZ. I'LL PROBABLY GET AN STD JUST BY BREATHING THIS AIR!

THERE'S NO WAY I'M GONNA FLUSH & LET THIS FECAL MATTER GO AERIAL. I'LL JUST PISS ON TOP &...

PSSSSS

OH MY GOD!

WHAT A BLAST FROM THE PAST!

ASSTEROIDS

OH MAN WHAT FUN!

EMPLOYEES MUST WASH HANDS 50% OF THE TIME

PSSSSSSSSSS

CLA-CLUNK

WELL THAT'S ABOUT ALL THERE IS TO THAT.

A HEART WARMING TALE, EH? WELL THERE IS A BIT OF A SAD SIDE TO IT..

FLUSH

YOU THINK WITH ALL THIS RETRO SHIT GOING ON NOW-IN-DAYS, PEOPLE WOULD BE DOWN WITH NOT FLUSHING AGAIN.

AS RARE AS IT WAS, IF I DIDN'T HAVE MY CURRENT SET-UP, I'D PROBABLY NEVER HAVE ANOTHER CHANCE TO PLAY!

MY EX IS DEAD

I KNOW YOU'RE THINKING: "BUT KAZ, YOU DON'T NEED ANOTHER PERSON'S POOP TO PLAY YOUR SICKO GAME...

YOU CAN USE YOUR OWN, CAN'T YOU?"

WELL YOU'RE WRONG.

YOU SEE...

MY EX D

I'M INCAPABLE OF PRODUCING FLOATERS.

THAT'S RIGHT. MY SHIT SINKS.

MY ENTIRE LIFE I'VE BEEN DEPRIVED DUE TO MY POOR DIET OF PEPSI, CANDY, TAQUITOS & ICE CREAM.

IT'S TRAGIC. WHILE OTHERS WASTE THEIR BUOYANT EXCREMENT, I'M CURSED WITH HEAVY FUDGEY SNAKE-LOGS.

BUT NOT TO WORRY. LIKE I SAID, I'VE COME UP WITH A SOLUTION...

EESIN'T DAT WITE MISTA FWUZZY?

MAN.

IF YOU THINK THIS IS GROSS, YOU SHOULD SEE WHEN HIS GIRLFRIEND COMES OVER & THEY PLAY "DIG DUG!"

♫ GOTTA GO GOTTA GO, GOTTA GO RIGHT NOW...

the end!

Youre driving through the countryside one night
and a car pulls up behind you
and nudges your bumper

The car accelerates
attempting to run you off the road
but you swerve
and the other car careens into a pond.

Matt Rota

You drive to a house in the distance
  hoping that someone can help
The people from the car
  are coming up the driveway after you.

You run through the open room
It's like an old school
unused for many years   The
stairs rise floor by floor beyond
what had seemed possible   from outside.

You enter an open room and inside it's a

bedroom with a girl cradling something dear

and crying   She never looks up

Not wanting to disturb her

you continue   upward to more rooms.

you continue   upward to more mysterious rooms
never lingering your pursuers are closing in
             It goes like this forever it seems.

until you
climb a flight of stairs
to a closed door
Bright light seeps out
under the door
and your entourage
is very close at hand now.

You turn the knob and open the door.
You and your company
stand shivering in the morning.

I FLEW TO NY CITY LAST WEEK.

I WENT WITH MELISSA

MELISSA IS MY EX-GIRLFRIEND

BUT SHE IS ALSO MY BEST FRIEND

LAURA IS BACK HOME

WE DATED FOR 3 YEARS AND ARE NOW BEST FRIENDS

SHE IS NOW IN BEAUTY SCHOOL

AND WE LIVE IN A HOUSE TOGETHER

BEEP

HONK

N.Y. IS A BIG AND DIRTY PLACE!

I WAS THERE TO PROMOTE MY 1ST BOOK

I WAS HAPPY TO GO HOME

HOME IS MILWAUKEE, WISCONSIN.

WHILE DRAWING THIS STORY...

I SAW A MAN GET ARRESTED OUTSIDE MY WINDOW.

AND I WONDER IF I WILL GO BACK TO N.Y. NEXT YEAR.

—MAX 6-18-05

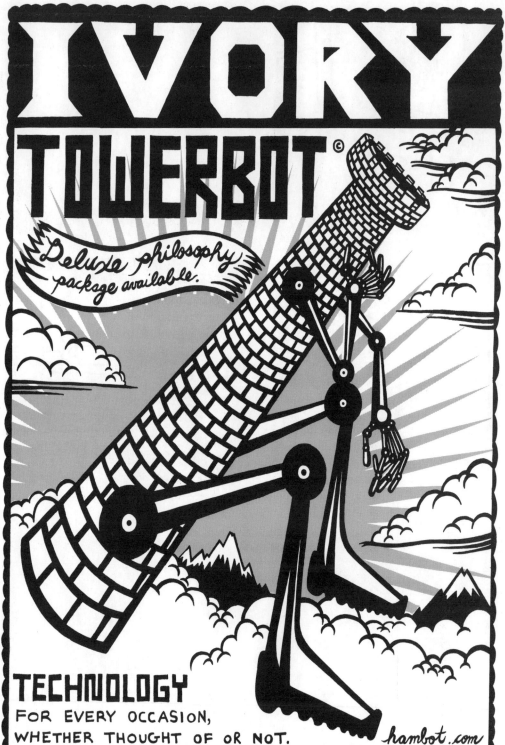

BREAKER BOYS

"ONCE A MINER, TWICE A BREAKER BOY.*"

COUGH COUGH HACK

THE DUST UP IN THIS TIPPLE...

...IS 'BOUT TA **KILL** ME.

OH·AH,

COUGH COUGH

COUGH

WHATCH YA NEED IS TA CHEW TABACCAH.

SPLURT!

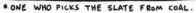

* ONE WHO PICKS THE SLATE FROM COAL.

Jeff Sharp

© JEFF SHARP

I'm setting up tables and chairs and art supplies... waiting for the kids to arrive when the fire alarm goes off.

Hani comes to collect me ... we all have to leave the building.

The rec. center staff bring me into a stairwell which stinks of urine... I'm careful not to step in the shit left on the landing...

Tenants have gathered in the apartment's lobby.. elevator doors are wide open going nowhere... sigh... just stand and wait...

Dave Lapp

Near the front door, three big teens are pushing and shoving two younger boys... play fighting... Ali, a <u>staff</u> member is there...

The play fighting continues a bit... then the big teen flattens the skinny kid with one really hard punch in the chest! Knocks the kid right to the floor!

Once flattened, the big teen punches the kid in the chest so hard I hear a horrible hollow sound that I've never heard before...

The other big teen joins in and kicks the kid in the ribs with the toe of his shoe, there's that sickening hollow sound again...

The kid remains on the floor while the teens stand around giving each other advice.

Amazingly the skinny kid gets up without crying or showing any signs of pain.

He walks slowly, stiffly... straight to the wall...

...where he stands very still.

The big teens bring the younger kid over and start shoving him into the skinny kid...

...they push them together until they start to 'play fight.'

The firemen have arrived. They're waiting to be let in, but the teens won't open the door! People start yelling at them...

... finally one of the other staff gets Ali's attention, and he casually 'buzzes' them in.

The firemen come tromping in and I feel relieved by their authoratative presence.

When I look back, the fighting's stopped and the youngest boy is gone...

... he comes back from the variety store and pulls a bottle of pop from beneath his shirt and presents it to Ali...

...it's a glass bottle and they can't open it, so they all come over to the elevator ... to go up and get a bottle opener?...

A fireman comes by and tells the guys that the elevator won't be going anywhere for quite awhile...

...so the two younger guys start play fighting again.

The older guys keep looking over their shoulders and eventually form a wall across the mouth of the elevator.

CHICKEN WING!

NELSON!

I can't see the fighting now, but I can hear loud thumps and thuds as the boys bang hard against the walls...

Finally the fire alarm stops...
I want to get away from this
miserable scene.

I take the 'piss' stairs back
down... I keep checking over
my shoulder... I feel like
those thugs are right behind
me...

I take a wrong turn and end
up at the gloomy parking
garage... if I'm gonna get
jumped, this is the place...

... I step back into the stairwell... no one's there, no
one's following me...

I get back to the art room and sit down...it reeks of pot smoke...I'm supposed to teach little kids in here.

No kids show up so I go to the gym and the guys from the lobby are there... the one kid's got the pop bottle...the top's been smashed off...

DON'T DRINK THAT! IT'LL CUT YOU UP INSIDE!

The kid's gonna drink from a broken, jagged edged bottle!!...There's four staff members just watching...finally Hani says something!...

...but, big smile, the kid drinks from it anyway.

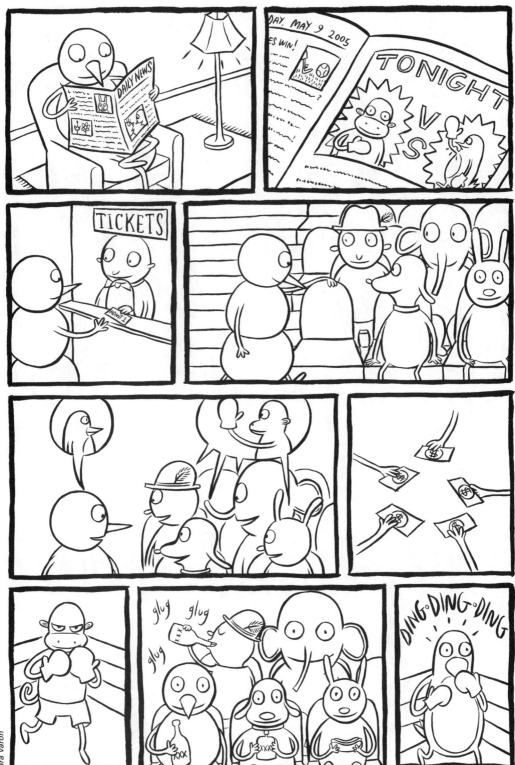

Sara Varon

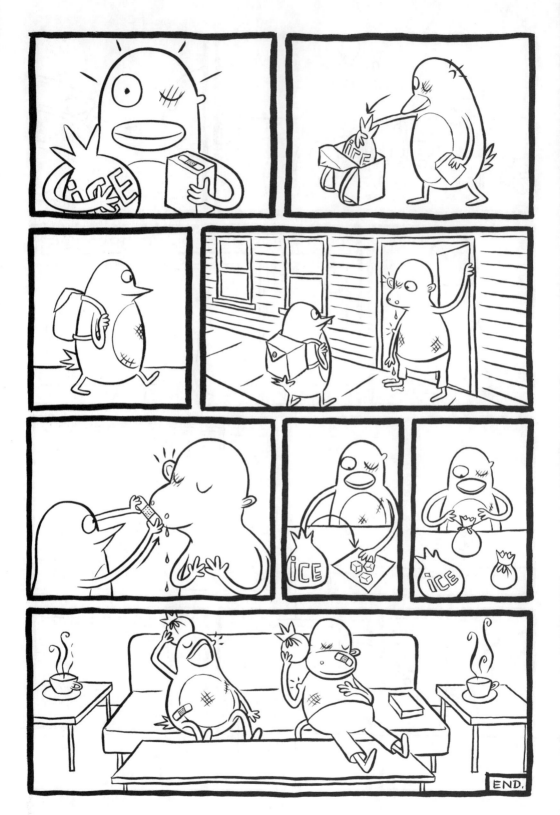

Nor should we forget that the deed
is but a reflex of the sentiment of many
thousand secession rulers and sympathizers.
For this they have watched—for this they have
prayed, and now the consequences will be visited
on their heads. — *Gloucester Telegraph,*
Wednesday, April 19, 1865.

THE GREAT CALAMITY

Words drawn from accounts in *The Gloucester
Telegraph* and James R. Pringle's 1892
"History of Gloucester." Illustrations
by Greg Cook in Gloucester, Mass., 2003.

The spirit exhibited in town on Wednesday, while there may
be much to excuse it, is *not safe* as a precedent. The
popular feeling, once carried beyond bounds, is exceedingly
hard to repress. If mob law may be invoked in a good cause,
it is quite as likely to be exhibited in a less worthy direction.
—*Gloucester Telegraph,* Saturday, April 22, 1865.

PUBLIC NOTICE:
Gloucester, Massachusetts.

ABRAHAM LINCOLN,
President of the United States, is no more.

Quite an excitement was raised in consequence of reports that persons had refused to display flags or had given expression to disloyal sentiments.

The crowd found
George Steele Jr.
Epes Porter
Thomas Hall
William T. Cooper
William Cogswell
Robert Rowe.

Salute the
national emblem!

KISS ITS FOLDS!

Give three
cheers for our flag!

A throng numbering some 800.

The residence of John Wheeler, an aged citizen whose two sons served their country in the war for the preservation of the Union.

Suspended astride a rail, Mr. Wheeler was borne through Washington and Front streets.

Render all the homage demanded, old man!

The Custom House, corner of Front and Pleasant streets.

After suffering severe indignities:

God bless **AMERICA.** I love this nation. HUZZAH.

It is not safe to array oneself against the popular sentiment!

Please disperse, my friends, my fellow citizens.

Addison Gilbert, chairman of Gloucester selectmen.

This is a sacred day.

Listen to the church bells now so solemnly tolling for the martyred dead.

For the good name of this town, please do not commit acts for which, in the future, you will express regret.

Reason asserted its sway and with these words of wisdom the multitude dispersed. Thus ended the most serious popular uprising recorded in the town's annals.

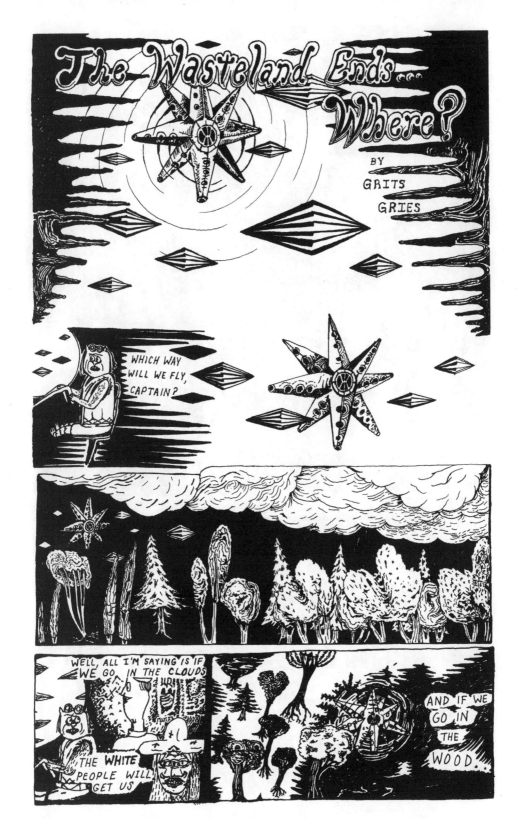

Sindre W. Goksøyr

Scott Morse

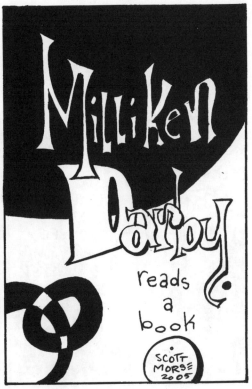

OK, WE'LL TRY IT OUT.

NOW, THE ANSWER'S THE THING, HERE, MISTER DARBY. IF YOU HAPPEN UPON IT, YOU NEED TO GIVE A HOLLAR AND LET US SEE WHAT YOU'VE DISCOVERED.

WE'RE ALL LOOKING FOR THE ANSWER, AND IT COULD LEAP OUT OF ANY BOOK HERE...

... AND SMACK ANY ONE OF US UPSIDE THE NOGGIN'.

SO YOU LET US KNOW IF YOU GET A GOOD WALLUP BY THE ANSWER. RIGHT, THEN?

RIGHT!

GOOD SHOW, DARBY.

NOW HAVE AT IT. YOU START WITH THIS ONE.

OF COURSE I WILL!

DIMENSION N

THAT FOOL WON'T CONTRIBUTE TO OUR PROGRESS.

HE PROBABLY CAN'T EVEN SOUND OUT SYLLABLES.

HEH. EINSTEIN ASKED THE QUESTIONS A CHILD MIGHT ASK, AND LOOK WHERE HE ENDED UP.

IT MIGHT TAKE SOMEONE A BIT MORE INNOCENT THAN OLD KNITTERS LIKE US TO UNRAVEL SOMETHING LIKE THE SUPERSTRING THEORY.

WHAT WORD IS THIS CURLY ONE?

Hmm?

THAT'S THE NUMBER OF THE PAGE YOU'RE ON, MY BOY. PAGE TWENTY-SEVEN.

AND POPULAR SCIENCE INDICATIONS THAT E MIGHT QUALIFY AS HAPPINESS, AND OTHE EMOTIONS AS DIMEN UNTO THEMSEL

FIG. 10

SKIP

MAYBE HE FOUND THE ANSWER?

I'M SURE HE DID.

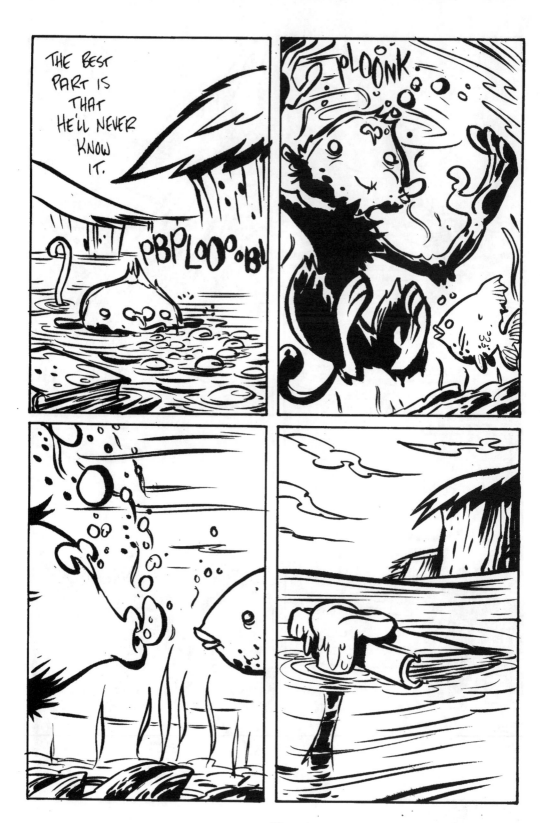

Martin Cendreda

A FEW HOURS LATER...

OH MAN, I DON'T FEEL SO HOT...

BETTER GET BACK TO WRITING...

UH-OH, I THINK I'M GONNA BE SSSICK...

HWARK!!

UNHMMM....

KA-THUNK!!

MAYBE I'LL START TOMORROW......

THE END.

Damien Jay

I went out to see my Father in Sacramento. I live in Berkeley now, and see him every few months.

HEY.

IS THE BEER COLD?

HOW'S YOUR MOM?

GOOD. THEY WENT TO DAN'S BROTHER'S FOR DINNER.

This is his "temporary apartment," where he moved a couple years after the divorce. He's been here thirteen years.

I'M GLAD YOU CAME BY TO PLAY. SEEMS LIKE ALL I DO IS WORK AND COME HOME AND FLOP THESE DAYS.

THANKS.

He passed the Bar a couple months ago and is starting on his fourth career, as a lawyer.

SO, I WANT TO DO A STORY ABOUT YOU AND SUSAN LIVING IN BERKELEY IN THE SIXTIES.

UH-HUH...

WHEN DID YOU FIRST MOVE THERE?

YOUR MOTHER AND I MOVED TO BERKELEY IN FEBRUARY OF 1968.

Jesse Reklaw

WE HAD **FIVE DOLLARS** BETWEEN US AND SLEPT ON THE BACK PORCH OF IAN AND KATIE'S HOUSE.

MORNING NEIGHBORS! ANYBODY UP FOR COFFEE?

UP!

I APPLIED FOR GARBAGE MAN IN THE CITY OF BERKELEY, AND THEY DIDN'T ACCEPT ME.

WHAT ARE WE GOING TO DO FOR **MONEY**?

SO, WE MET THESE GUYS WHO LIVED AT THE **DKE** FRATERNITY HOUSE.

HEY MAN, WHAT'S HAPPENING?

NUTHIN', MAN.

WE'RE HAVING A LITTLE **GATHERING** AT OUR HOUSE THIS SATURDAY...

LISTEN TO SOME TUNES, SMOKE SOME GRASS...

WANNA GO?

RIGHT ON!

THERE WAS SUPPOSED TO BE **FORTY-SOME-ODD** PEOPLE IN THAT FRAT HOUSE, BUT THERE WAS ONLY **FOURTEEN**. THESE GUYS WERE A BUNCH OF DOPERS, JUST **FAKING** THEIR WAY THROUGH CLASSES. THEY WERE SELLING THE PERSIAN RUGS FROM THE HOUSE FOR **DOPE MONEY**.

THEY HAD A PARTY THERE EVERY WEEKEND. WE WOULD ALWAYS GO OVER THERE AND SMOKE **WEED** AND SMOKE **OPIUM**, THEY TRADED THIS ONE PERSIAN RUG FOR, I DUNNO, A **POUND** OF OPIUM.

ONE NIGHT WE HAD THIS IDEA...

HEY, CAN WE USE YOUR KITCHEN DOWNSTAIRS TO MAKE FOOD AND **SELL** IT?

SURE, MAN, WHATEVER... **HEY** - PASS THAT **JOINT!**

SO OUT OF THAT **PIPE DREAM** CAME THE BAKERY CART. I BUILT A PLYWOOD BOX, AND GOT SOME OLD WAGON WHEELS, WHICH I LACQUERED UP, THEN PAINTED THE SEALED WAX.

WE ROLLED IT DOWN THE HILL EACH MORNING AND THEN PUSHED IT UP THE FUCKING HILL.

ORGANIC FOOD

YOUR MOTHER AND I WERE MAKING ABOUT **TEN DOLLARS** A DAY SELLING ORGANIC FOOD IN FRONT OF THE UNIVERSITY.

WAS TELEGRAPH AVENUE COVERED WITH ALL THE **VENDORS** SELLING TIE-DYE AND INCENSE, LIKE IT IS NOW EVERY WEEKEND?

THERE WERE A FEW...

BUT THIS WAS **BEFORE** THEY HAD THE EXTRA-WIDE SIDEWALKS, SO THERE WASN'T MUCH ROOM FOR VENDORS.

BACK THEN PEOPLE'S PARK WAS JUST A BIG **VACANT AREA.** THERE WERE A LOT OF PEOPLE HANGING OUT ALL THE TIME... IT WAS REAL **CASUAL.**

ONE NIGHT THERE GOT TO BE SUCH A MASS OF PEOPLE — LITTLE JUG BANDS ON THE CORNERS, BEARDED HIPPIES, PEOPLE GETTING HIGH, ON ACID...

IT ERUPTED INTO THIS BIG STREET PARTY, UP SEVERAL BLOCKS OF TELEGRAPH AND INTO SPROUL PLAZA. THIS WAS THE FIRST *BERKELEY FREE STREET PARTY*.

IT **SHUT DOWN** THE MERCHANTS AND WENT ON ALL NIGHT.

WOW! SOUNDS LIKE FUN!

YEAH, AND A GREAT PLACE TO GET HIGH FOR **FREE**.

BUT THE NEXT NIGHT THE POLICE CAME AND *TEARGASSED EVERYBODY*.

ANOTHER THING WE DID WAS...IF YOU DIDN'T HAVE ANY DOPE, YOU COULD GO OUT ON TELEGRAPH NEAR ASHBY AND HITCHHIKE UP TO THE UNIVERSITY.

BEFORE LONG, SOME FREAKS WOULD COME ALONG IN A VOLKSWAGEN BUS AND PICK YOU UP AND GET YOU HIGH.

YOU GUYS WANT A **TOKE**?

HA-HA-HA! HOW MANY TIMES DID YOU DO THAT?

DOZENS.

BUT AROUND THAT TIME I MET THESE GUYS WHO WERE GOING DOWN TO MEXICO AND GETTING REALLY **GOOD** WEED.

= CAR DOOR =

Removable panel

screws

Bags of Dope

THEY'D REMOVED THE SIDE PANEL FROM THEIR CAR DOOR AND WOULD STASH A FEW **POUNDS** OF DOPE IN THERE TO GET THROUGH BORDER INSPECTION.

I BOUGHT IT FOR $125 A POUND, AND LATER MAYBE AS LOW AS $100. A **LOT** MORE THAN OTHERS.

COZ THIS WAS THE GOOD STUFF?

YEAH! PEOPLE WERE ALWAYS ASKING ABOUT IT.

WOW MAN, WHERE'D YOU GET THIS SHIT?

SO I FIGURED IF I TOOK TWO OR THREE LIDS DOWN IN THE **BAKERY CART**, I'D PROBABLY MAKE A **HELL** OF A LOT MORE MONEY THAN SELLING ORGANIC FOOD TO HIPPIES.

SO I DID THAT A **COUPLE** OF TIMES AND...

I FOUND IT **SCARY.**

HEE HEE.

HOW DID PEOPLE KNOW YOU WERE SELLING DOPE? I MEAN WAS THERE A **SIGNAL,** OR...?

THEY WERE PEOPLE I KNEW FROM HANGING OUT ON THE AVENUE. A LOT OF PEOPLE YOU KNEW FROM JUST HANGING OUT, OR SEEING THEM AT CONCERTS.

SO YOU NEVER ASKED A STRANGER, "HEY YOU WANT SOME GOOD DOPE WITH THAT *BRAN MUFFIN?"*

NAHH!

AND SEE, MOST PEOPLE DIDN'T SELL A FULL OUNCE IN THEIR LIDS. THEY HAD MAYBE ONLY 3/4 OF AN OUNCE. BUT I WOULD WEIGH IT WITH AN **OHAUS TRIPLE-BEAM** SCALE.

I REMEMBER THAT SCALE FROM WHEN I WAS A KID!

UH-HUH. THEN YOUR MOTHER HAD SOME COLORED YARN WE WOULD TIE THE BAGGIES WITH.

WAS THAT LIKE YOUR TRADEMARK? THIS IS THE GOOD STUFF, A FULL OUNCE, THE COLORED YARN MEANS YOUR WEED IS GUARANTEED?

YOUR WEED IS GUARANTEED! IT'S ALL YOU'LL EVER NEED!

BUT AN OUNCE, THAT'S A LOT, RIGHT? I MEAN, PEOPLE BUY IT BY THE **EIGHTH** OUNCE THESE DAYS...

YEAH, AN EIGHTH WILL RUN YA $50 OR SOMETHING.

BUT I WAS SELLING LIDS FOR $12.50, AND WITH 16 OUNCES IN A POUND... LET'S SEE... I WAS MAKING ALMOST **DOUBLE** MY MONEY.

AND THEN THE PEOPLE SELLING *PLASTIC FOOD* IN FRONT OF THE UNIVERSITY, CORN-ON-THE-COB, HOT DOGS AND SNO-CONES, THEY WERE MAKING SO MUCH MONEY THEY WANTED A **SECOND** FOOD CART.

THEY ASKED US TO RUN IT, SO WE'D MAKE LIKE **EIGHTY** BUCKS A WEEK DOING THAT. AND ON THE WEEKENDS WE'D MAKE ALMOST AS MUCH AT THE ROCK CONCERTS SELLING HOT DOGS AND SNO-CONES TO THE HIPPIES.

THIS WAS IN THE PARK ACROSS FROM THE BERKELEY CITY HALL, ON GROVE STREET, WHICH IS NOW *MARTIN LUTHER KING BOULEVARD.* ALL KINDS OF BANDS PLAYED THERE FOR FREE ON THE WEEKENDS: STEVE MILLER, QUICKSILVER MESSENGER SERVICE,...

...JERRY GARCIA BAND, BIG BROTHER AND THE HOLDING COMPANY, CANNED HEAT, COUNTRY JOE AND THE FISH... IT WAS *REAL* POPULAR.

DID YOU SELL **DOPE** OUT OF THE CART AT CONCERTS?

NO, THAT WAS TOO CONSPICUOUS.

BUT I HAD A GUITAR CASE I CARRIED, AND MET PEOPLE AT THEIR HOUSES. I WAS TRYING TO GET THE $300 TO PAY FOR YOUR SISTER'S **BIRTH.**

SUCH A RESPONSIBLE FATHER!

YUP.

©2005 JESSE REKLAW

Sir Ernest Shackleton in:
PATIENCE CAMP
a cartoon account of a historical event by N.U.Bertozzi

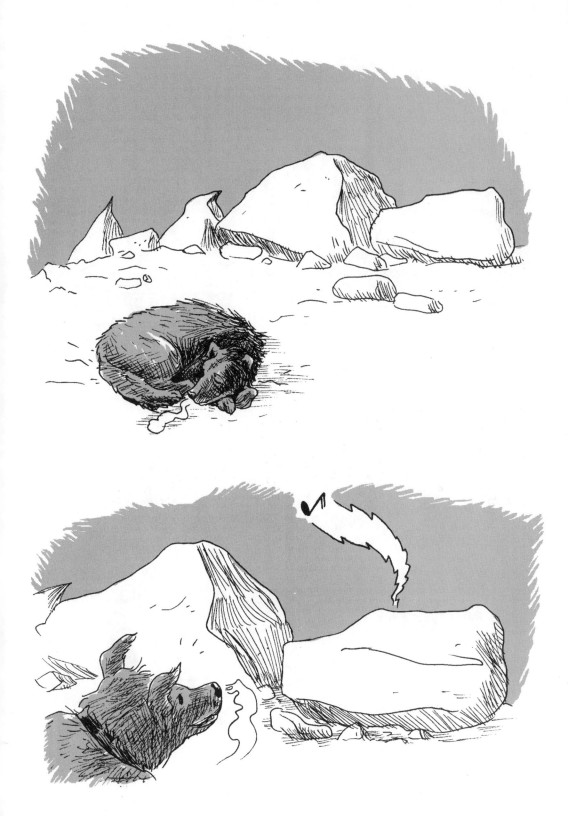

Wild loved the dogs.

I'm sorry for Wild but my men have to eat.

Morale was no better at camp...

I suppose I'd underestimated the effect, that putting down the dogs would have on the crew.

Boys.

Boss.

Finding ways for the men to blow off steam has become a daily challenge.

Football is the most often-used recourse.

Sadly, even today's three rounds of game were unable to soothe men's souls.

Punishment is out of the question; you can't threaten to take away a man's rum ration if there isn't a drop for a thousand miles.

This wound would continue to fester amongst my crew. Not a physical wound, but a spiritual affliction.

To heal the spirit is a far more difficult task than setting a leg or suturing a gash.

To relieve suffering of the soul I find the arts to be a most perfect balm.

We would have an evening of entertainment. The two antagonists, Wild and Orde-Lees, would be given the task of performing in a drama together, ostensibly for the Greater Good.

A stage was constructed by the capable McNeish, costumes were sewn, a rehearsal was held in my tent, a dinner of pemican with extra seal blubber was served, and we were ready.

We set up an extra stove and a brace of oil candles the men huddled close to the stage and I began with a few lines from Browning.

...Ah but a man's reach should exceed his grasp.

Or what's a Heaven for?

Perhaps I began with many lines of Browning...

That far land *that* we dream about,

Where every man is his own architecht.

We then commenced with an abridged and somewhat improvised 'Twelfth Night'. The sight of Orde-Lees as a maid was a delight and an enchantment to all.

What country, friend, is this?

It is Illyria, lady.

HA!

HOO!

MARRY ME!

I can speak without equivocation that no audience ever loved a troupe of players more than ours. As for the feud between Orde-Lees and Wild, it was put to bed at least for a time.

After the drama we entreated Hussey to lead us on his banjo. We sang an ode to every one of Her Majesty's green valleys and to every woman who lived therein.

Are you sailing away, Donald Hugh?

Then don't forget to stow an English Rose!

It was pleasing to think that, at the very end of the Earth our tiny congregation of twenty-eight souls could muster a sound that warmed the barren landscape for miles.

And so we passed safely through another day on the ice. What great, and noble hearts have these men, each and every one!

for Liz, it's about smiling to a stranger

and she feels **happy** when a stranger smiles to her.

Chao was stuck so a stranger helped her out

Now that stranger is her friend. :)

There's nothing strange about kindness

Brielle treated herself to a new book

and gave it to a friend. So she could have a **look**

Luke Ramsey

FOR STEPHANIE

"it's about going out of your way to appreciate someone's efforts."

He also likes to remind friends of who they are

mary feels happy about

giving up her comfy window seat, so two people can be happy.

Brooke wanted a job where she could help people

So, some good people helped her find that job.

Jason spared some change to a hungry man.

But when Jason was hungry. He had no money left. So, his roommate bought him his favourite lunch.

KRS-ONE said "that kindness is giving to someone if it doesn't hurt that person."

To pinpoint what would benefit, someone's needs.

PAIN KILLERS or ?

Justin showed his friend a suprise, to make her smile.

she loved it So much. So, she suprised Justin with a drawing...

For Aryon, it's about helping someone. With no expectations.

And, it's a **joy** when the **help** is **appreciated.**

all for you

Mark feels that it is important to look out for others...

by helping to carry someone's weight for a while. May make you smile.

Andrew offered his skills for a non-profit art benefit

After the gig. He was tired and hungry. So, his girlfriend prepared a warm, tasty meal.

it's about caring

A friend took the time to tell Alex that she was thinking **Of him.**

SOUL

believes kindness is one self as everyone

to respect others as you'd want to be respected.

The ground we walk on. Never looses contact with the water that the fish swim in. The water evaporates into the sky, where the birds fly towards the stars, that shine apon us all.

Amy was a child, the last time she had a birthday bash.

So she felt young again when her friends threw her a party SUPRISE

Bradford's friend made him a personal gift.

(•) Bradford (•) loves his friend so much, because they can always cut to the core with each other.

for Jesse, it's about sharing your last slice with a friend, even though you haven't eaten all day.

It's about allowing others to be. Giving people the freedom to live the life they want, without prejudice towards their choices.

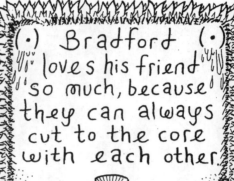

Damian feels kindness is offering comfort to someone

generosity

always gives more to you than it takes

Alex told a stranger that they had toilet paper stuck to their foot.

A friend told Alex that he had some food stuck in his teeth

Taj's Mom teaches him about having a passion for life. And, she gives the best hugs.

So, Taj wants to love others like the way his mom loves him.

Becky enjoys baking treats for her pals.

Her friends made a big "Becky Appreciation Day" cake, to thank her for their friendships.

Joe Derry

Brendan Burford

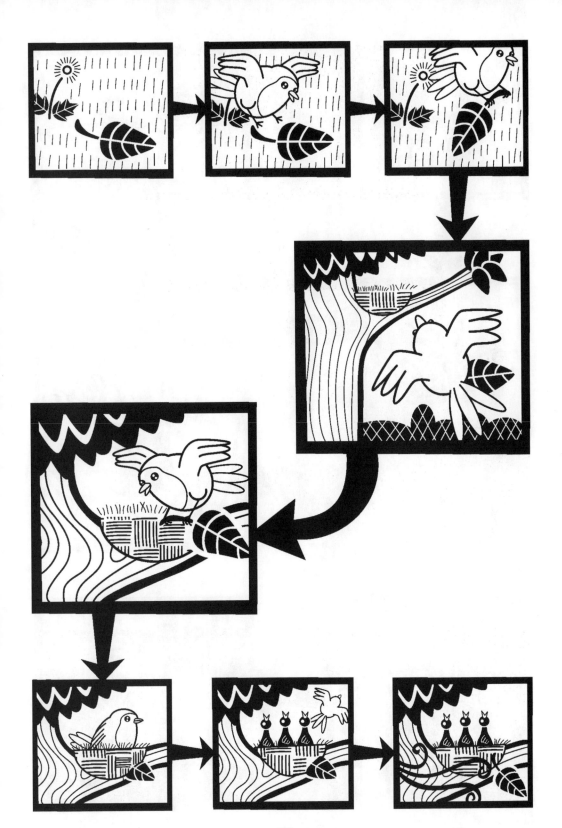

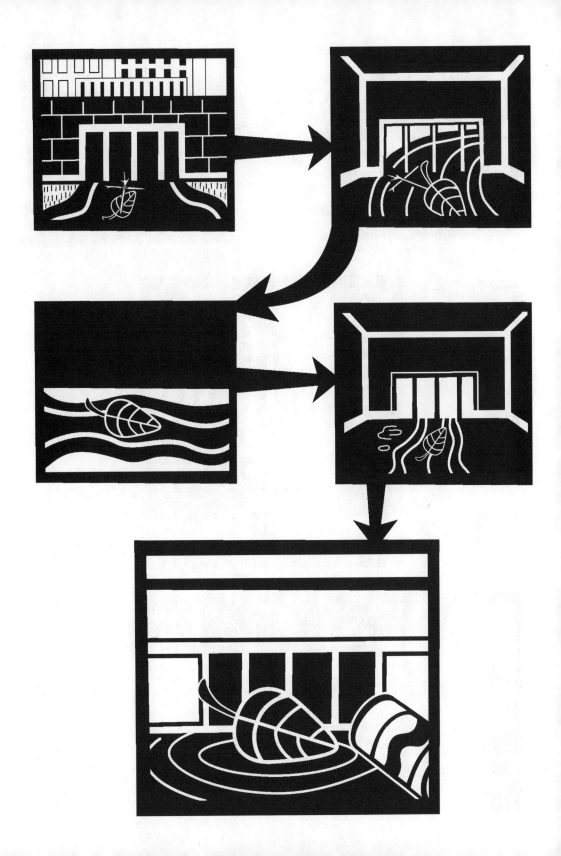

By day he cleans up your office, by night he cleans up the streets: Alan Diesler, a.k.a. Afrodisiac! A mysterious man from a far-away land— the original unbeatable, irresistible, smooth dark chocolate brother, bitch!

AFRODISIAC

IT'S NOT THE SIZE OF THE GOD IN THE FIGHT

Wilkesborough used to be a thrivin' town.

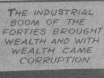

The industrial boom of the forties brought wealth and with wealth came corruption.

The corruption spawned a darkness that swallowed the daylight.

It's gettin' to be so honest folks like you or me can't go out at night.

STORY — MARUCA   STORY/ART — RUGG

JUST THEN, A GIANT BURSTS THROUGH THE DOOR, HUNGRY FOR ACTION!

WHERE DOS'T THOU HOPE TO HIDE, FAIR WENCH?!

DARK-SKINNED MORTAL, FETCH *HERCULES* A PINT OF ALE, SO THAT HE MIGHT SLAKE HIS *IMMENSE* THIRST!

WHO THE ⊕#✳! ARE YOU SUPPOSED TO BE?

BEHOLD! A GOD DEIGNS TO WALK AMONGST THEE! *I* AM *HERCULES!* FAVORED SON OF *ZEUS!*

NOW, LARGE-HAIRED *MONKEY*, SERVE THY GOD WELL AND THOU SHALL BE *REWARDED!*

WITH A PANTHER'S FEROCITY, THE AFRODISIAC STRIKES THE MASSIVE, IGNORANT IMMORTAL.

TAKIN' YOUR HIDE APART'LL BE MY REWARD, HONKY!

THUMP!

DAMN! CAT'S SKIN'S AS THICK AS LEATHER.

SO, TIS A *FIGHT* THOU DESIRES? TIS A *FIGHT* THOU HAST *FOUND*, FOOLISH MORTAL!

REMEMBERING THE SAGE WISDOM OF HIS OLD PARTNER, TRICKY DICK*, AFRODISIAC REALIZES BRUTE FORCE ALONE AIN'T GONNA JIVE.

GOTTA TAKE THE FIGHT OUTTA HIM...

*RICHARD NIXON

DICK LEARNED THE HARD WAY*, "GUILE AND RESOURCEFULNESS CAN OVERCOME SUPERIOR FIREPOWER." AN' I NEVER SAW THAT N'&&@ GET BEAT DOWN AGAIN.

OOUPH! BY GODS DEFIED...

BOOM!

*VIETNAM

THOU FIGHTS... DIRT-

THIS IS NO WAY TO TREAT THE SON O-

KRACK!

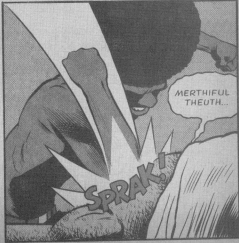

MERTHIFUL THEUTH...

SPRAK!

HERE'S YOUR ⊕#★!IN' ALE, TURKEY!

BEHOLD, A TITAN'S MIGHT PULVERIZED BY OBSIDIAN HAMMER FURY! HALF A WORLD AWAY, MT. OLYMPUS WEEPS.

ALYSHA, CHECK THIS SKIRT FOR MORE GOLD.

LATER THAT NIGHT.

HEY WENCH, ANOTHER ROUND OF ALE!

YETH, THIR.

THE END

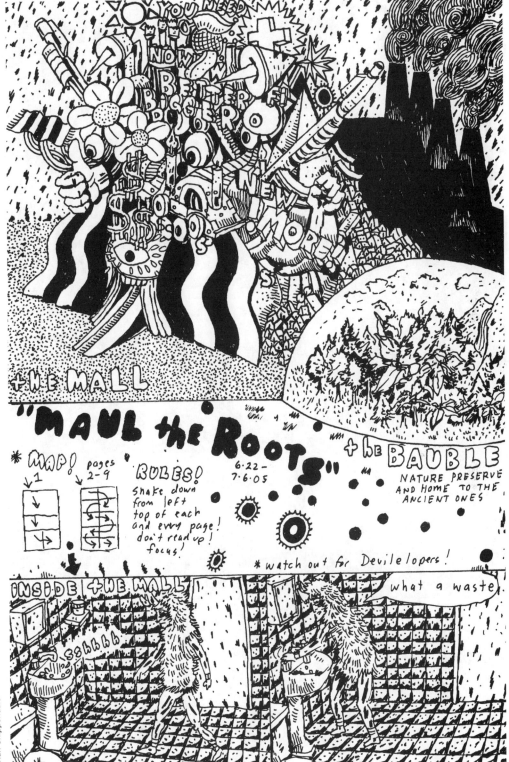

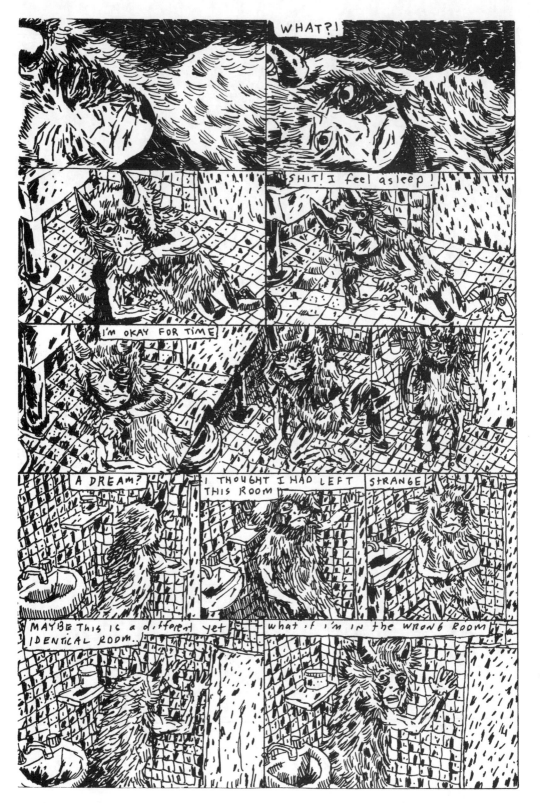

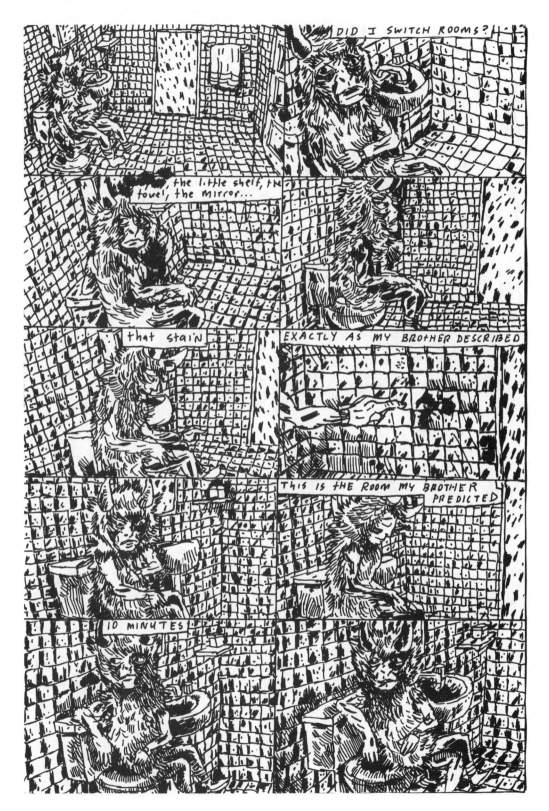

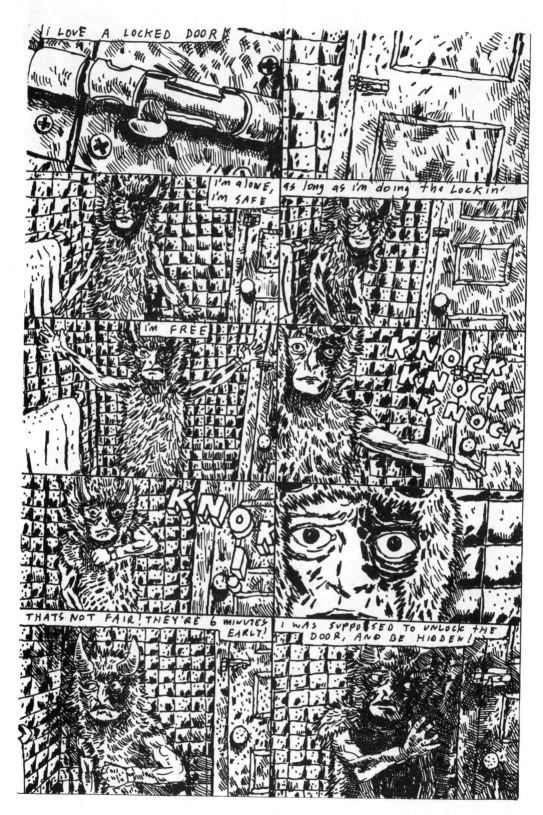

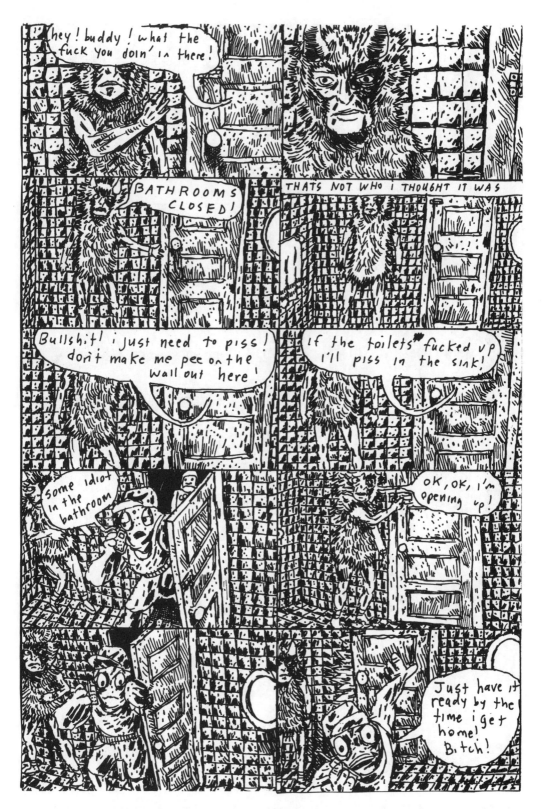

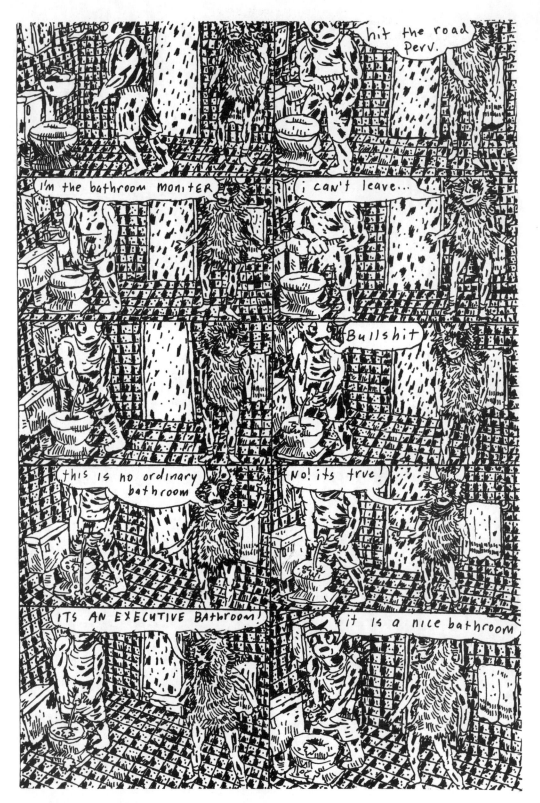

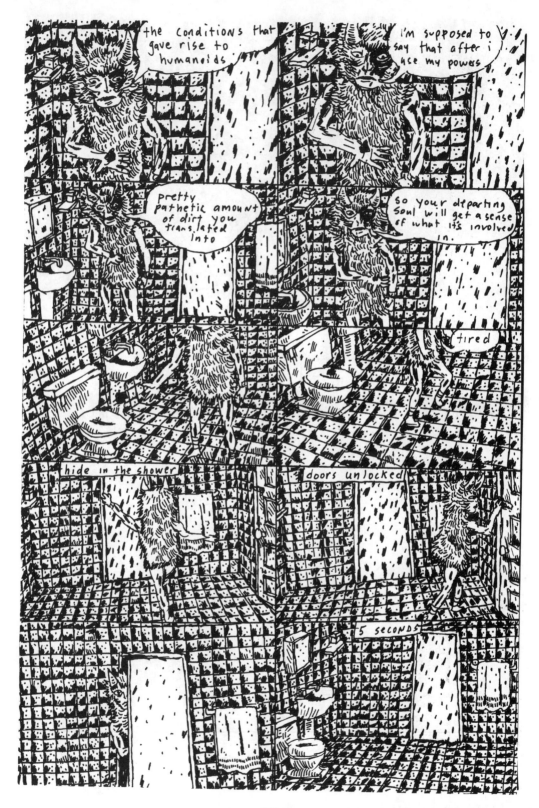

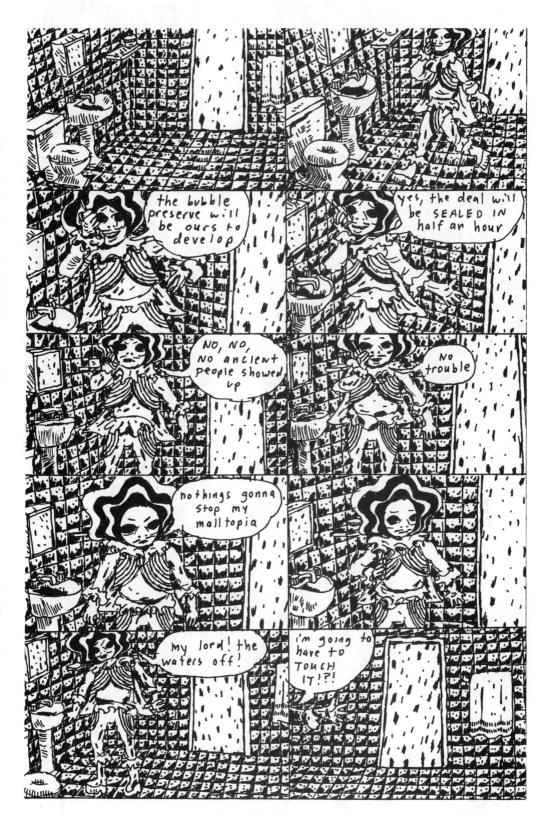

Monster Mouth Comics
by: Scott C.
holyshit! we're in a fuckin monster mouth!
i fuckin' know!
what the hell're we gonna do?
try to get the heck out of this dangerous spot!
good idea, bro!
i know it is!
how're we going to do it?
i do not know, my bro!
i'm totally freaking out right now!
me too! holy crap!
aaaagh!
aaa aaaagh!
fuckin aaaagh!
aaaagh! aaaagh!
wait! wait!
what? what?
maybe we should yell "help" instead of "aagh".
Yeah. Ok.
heeelp!
fuckin heeellp!

awesome! i sure am glad to be out of that monster mouth.
i know it! i don't even care that we're falling right now.
me neither! i never thought i'd love falling so much!
it feels way better than a monster mouth.
very true, my good bro.
man. i hope we land in a river. or on some hay.
yeah. or on pillows.
oh, totally. pillows would be best, probably.
oh, dope! a thatched roof!
a super soft thatched roof!
yayhay! lucky day for us!
woohoo! make way for the survivors!
the end.

R. Sikoryak

R2-D2 IS AN INDIE ROCKER

Jeff Czekaj

I HAVE COME TO MONSTER iSLAND TO TELL YOU THAT THE BOOK PUBLISHING AND ANiMATiON iNDUSTRIES ARE **COMPLETELY** DiFFERENT THAN THE MUSIC iNDUSTRY.

ALL OF YOUR "PROJECTS" WiLL BE ARTiSTiC **AND** FiNANCiAL SUCCESSES. **NO ONE** WiLL BE LEFT BEHiND. YOUR TRiUMPHS WiLL BE **MERiT-BASED**, NOT BASED ON WHO'S BEST AT "NETWORKiNG" OR WHOSE WORK iS PERCEiVED AS "MARKETABLE." AND, SO...

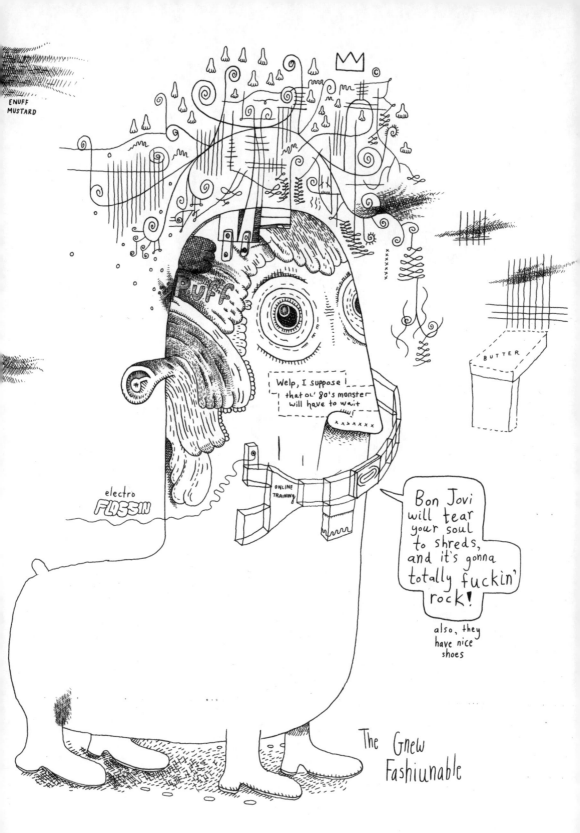

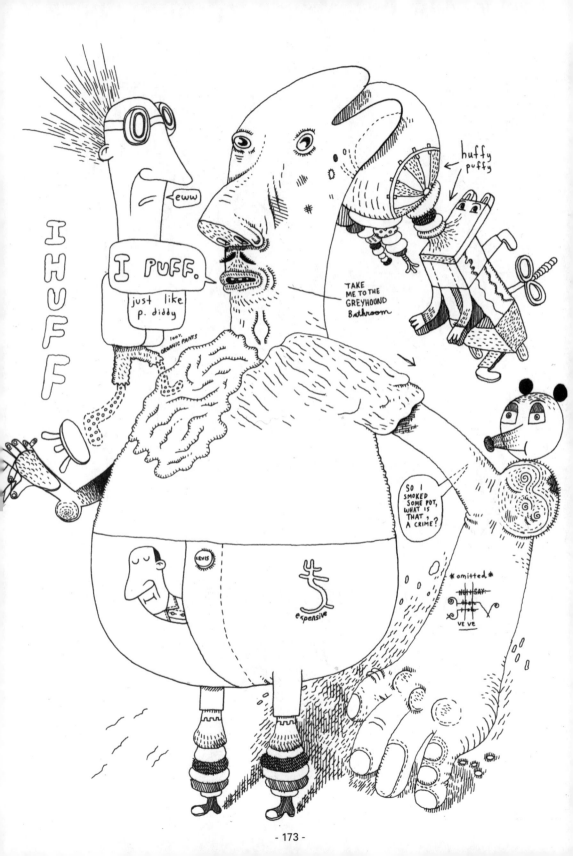

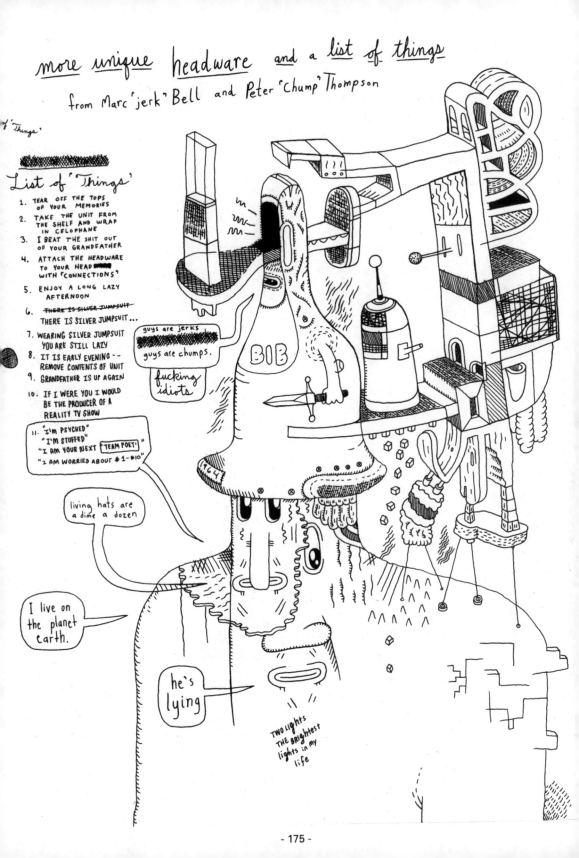

more unique headware and a list of things

from Marc "jerk" Bell and Peter "Chump" Thompson

List of "Things"

1. TEAR OFF THE TOPS OF YOUR MEMORIES
2. TAKE THE UNIT FROM THE SHELF AND WRAP IN CELOPHANE
3. I BEAT THE SHIT OUT OF YOUR GRANDFATHER
4. ATTACH THE HEADWARE TO YOUR HEAD ~~BRAINS~~ WITH "CONNECTIONS"
5. ENJOY A LONG LAZY AFTERNOON
6. ~~THERE IS SILVER JUMPSUIT~~ THERE IS SILVER JUMPSUIT...
7. WEARING SILVER JUMPSUIT YOU ARE STILL LAZY
8. IT IS EARLY EVENING -- REMOVE CONTENTS OF UNIT
9. GRANDFATHER IS UP AGAIN
10. IF I WERE YOU I WOULD BE THE PRODUCER OF A REALITY TV SHOW
11. "I'M PSYCHED"
    "I'M STUFFED"
    "I AM YOUR NEXT 'TEAM POET'"
    "I AM WORRIED ABOUT #1-#10"

guys are jerks
~~~~~~~~
guys are chumps.

fucking idiots

BIB

1964

living hats are a dime a dozen

I live on the planet earth.

he's lying

TWO LIGHTS THE BRIGHTEST lights in my life

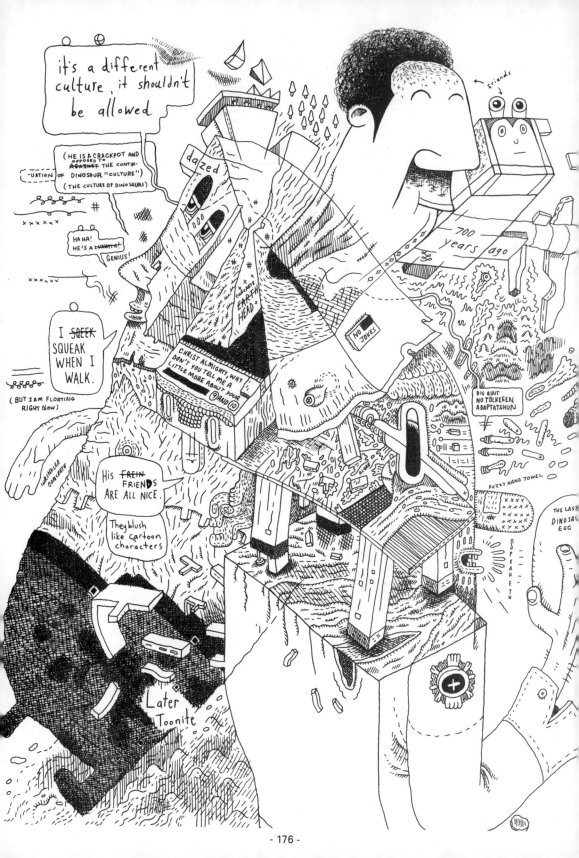

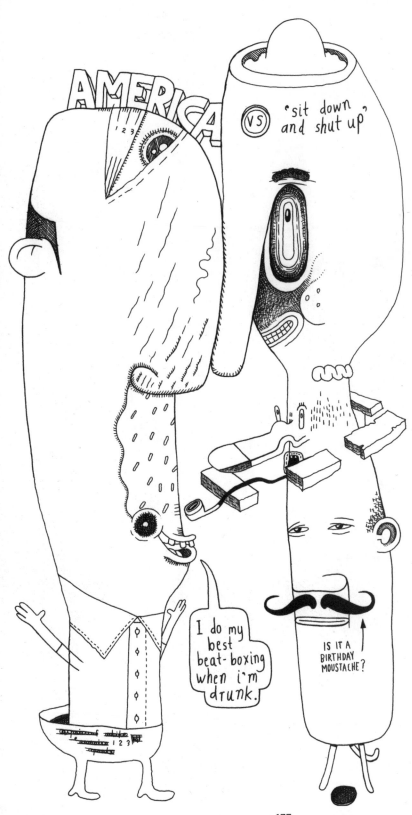

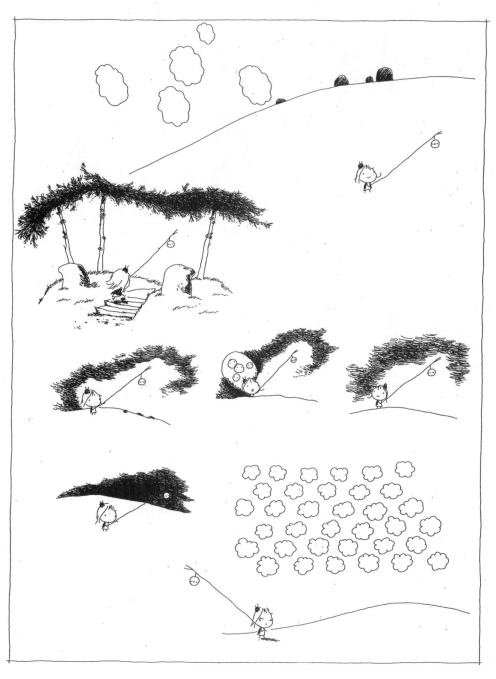

Vinh Ngo

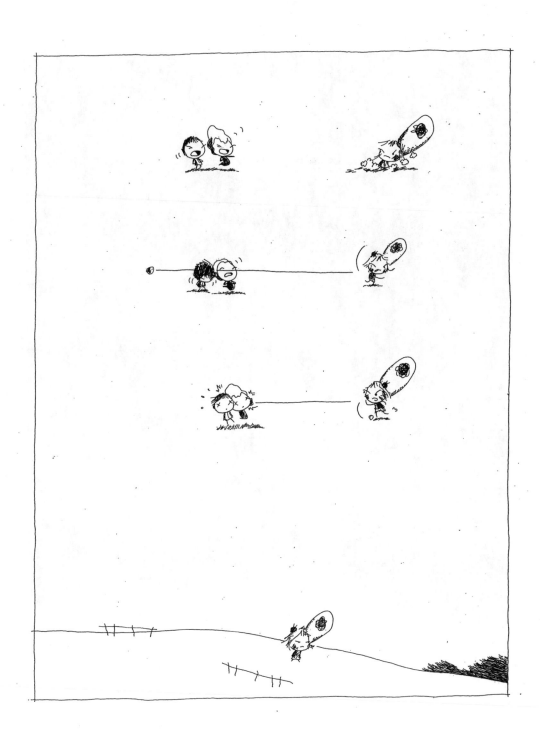

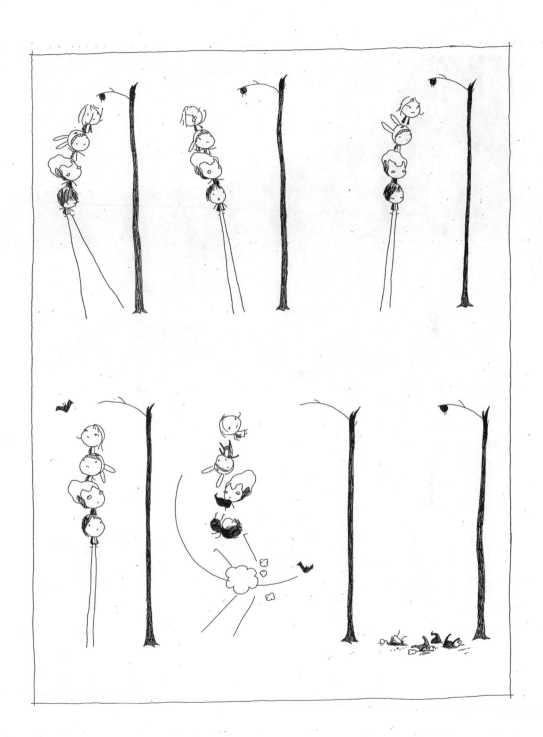

Maris Wicks

MARIS 05

SPX 2005